Explode The Code® 2nd Edition

6

Essential lessons for phonics mastery

Nancy Hall • Rena Price

EDUCATORS PUBLISHING SERVICE
Cambridge and Toronto

Cover art: Hugh Price
Text illustrations: Laura Price, Alan Price, Kelly Kennedy

Printed in Mayfield, PA, in January 2023
ISBN 978-0-8388-7806-4

9 10 PAH 24 23

Lesson 1

ar says /är/ as in *star*.

Read, write, and ◯ it.

car			
car			

farm			

card			

yarn			

scarf			

mark			

sparks			

ar says /är/ as in *st<u>ar</u>*.

⬭ the word that matches the picture.

(cart) or cat?

car or care?

march or match?

shark or shack?

happy or harp?

jar or jab?

hard or hand?

smell or snarl?

Spell. Write.

	(p) b	ai (ar)(k)	h	_park_____
	q c	ar a	f t	_____
	sh sc	an ar		_____
	h n	ar a	m n	_____
	h m	ar er	p t	_____
	d b	ar or	n h	_____
	sl sh	ai ar	k ke	_____

3

Yes or no?

	Yes	No
Can yellow yarn grow longer in the garden?	☐	☒
Will a chicken have dinner in the barnyard?	☐	☐
Do the stars and planets shine in the daytime?	☐	☐
Can a winter scarf be made of candy?	☐	☐
Can an army on the hillside see in the darkness?	☐	☐
Would it be smart to swim in a sea filled with sharks?	☐	☐
Will a market sell milk and eggs and apples to a shopper?	☐	☐

the word that matches the picture.

spangle speaker (sparkle)	peaking parking prankster
tangle target tarnish	archer artist arches
yardstick backyard yearling	party sparkly parking
target markers market	darted barking darkness
army arm armband	chopper charcoal charmer

Pick the best word to finish each sentence.

carpet	radar	~~target~~
marble	garden	marching
barnyard	varnish	charcoal

Carl tosses bean bags at the ___target___ .

The band is playing and _____ quickly
to the music.

A fuzzy _____ feels soft on the bottom
of your feet.

A match starts the _____ in the grill for hot dogs.

If you plant seeds in the _____ , tiny plants
will grow.

He paints _____ on the table to protect it
and make it shine.

The farmer keeps all the animals in the _____ .

X it.

Marvin throws a marble on the carpet.	☒	
Marvin keeps a dog mattress inside his car.	☐	
The shark swam with a dive mask and a snorkel.	☐	
The shark, dressed in a scarf and bathrobe, sang well.	☐	
The stars sparkle in the darkness.	☐	
It is hard for Arnold to park cars in the darkness.	☐	
The harp plays music and makes the party lively.	☐	
The harp plays music and makes the pigpen lively.	☐	
The ants are marching from the garden.	☐	
The army marches to the biggest target.	☐	
The man in the car likes the stars.	☐	
The cart is parked in the barnyard.	☐	
The careless artist drops her deck of cards in the barnyard.	☐	
The artist will varnish his cart.	☐	

Write it, using a word with *ar*.

	farm

Lesson 2

or says /ôr/ as in *fo**r**k*.

Read, write, and ⬭ it.

horn			
_____			

snore			
_____			

fort			
_____			

thorn			
_____			

horse			
_____			

porch			
_____			

store			
_____			

9

or says /ôr/ as in *f<u>or</u>k*.

◯ the word that matches the picture.

sport   or   spot?

cork   or   coat?

shop   or   short?

north   or   note?

born   or   bone?

stork   or   stock?

can   or   corn?

stone   or   storm?

	t	f	or	ar	l	k	_____
	p	c	oa	or	m	n	_____
	th	tr	er	or	n	u	_____
	ch	c	or	o	n	ne	_____
	b	t	or	oo	ct	ch	_____
	s	c	o	or	b	d	_____
	sh	st	or	oa	m	ne	_____

Yes or no?

	Yes	No
Will you bake a shortcake on a sunny morning?	☐	☐
Can a windy storm begin in a harbor?	☐	☐
Do Barby and a classmate ride horseback in a rowboat?	☐	☐
Can a lazy stork relax on the porch swing?	☐	☐
Can a dark forest be filled with sharp thorns?	☐	☐
Do you like to order corn on the cob for supper?	☐	☐
Can a hornet drive a speeding sports car in the sky?	☐	☐

forty fortress forgotten		store stormy story	
hornpipe horseback hospital		snoring moaning morning	
barber harbor harder		forty frothy lordly	
hopeful horses hornet		shortcake shorthand shoreline	
rather raisin razor		shortcut sports car sparkler	

13

Pick the best word to finish each sentence.

pork chop	organ	thorny
snort	stores	harbor
corner	forest	shortcake

You use both your hands and your feet to play music on
the _____ .

A horse may _____ when it is running fast.

A _____ is a flavorful meat you may have
for dinner.

There are many big trees in the dark green _____ .

A _____ plant will feel sharp if you step on
it with bare feet.

If you are shopping for a gift, you may visit many
_____ .

Big ships and other boats can stay for a long time in the
_____ .

X it.

The stork will fly north in the spring.	☐	
The stork sings on the porch.	☐	
A big shortcake was left on the porch.	☐	
A short rake is used to divide the corn.	☐	
The story tells of a horn on top of the fort.	☐	
There are forty horses in the store.	☐	
The organ is playing in the hall.	☐	
Ugly thorns are growing in the orchard.	☐	
Carl forgot to order a big milk shake.	☐	
Carl gets a big fork with his shortcake.	☐	
A dark morning can be the start of a stormy day.	☐	
The children play lots of sports in the morning.	☐	
The dark horse snorted and kicked its feet.	☐	
The sleepy hornet snores on top of the fort.	☐	

Write it, using a word with *or*.

	_____
	_____
	_____
	_____
	_____
	_____
	_____

Lesson 3

er, ir, and ur say /er/ as in
h<u>er</u>, b<u>ir</u>d, and b<u>ur</u>n.

Read, write, and ⬭ it.

stir			
_____			
curl			
_____			
serve			
_____			
dirt			
_____			
perch			
_____			
skirt			
_____			
nurse			
_____			

er, ir, and *ur* say /er/ as in *h<u>er</u>*, *b<u>ir</u>d*, and *b<u>ur</u>n*.

⬭ the word that matches the picture.

turn   or   torn?

fits   or   first?

jerk   or   park?

shirt   or   short?

disturb   or   dirty?

farm   or   fern?

porch   or   perch?

chirp   or   sharp?

	d b	ur ar	m n	_____
	j p	er ar	k ch	_____
	ch sh	ir or	p t	_____
	f t	or ur	u n	_____
	th tr	ai ir	b d	_____
	b d	ir ea	t b	_____
	ch cl	ar ur	th ch	_____

Yes or no?

	Yes	No
Can a person get dirty in a mud puddle?	☐	☐
Can thirty planes land as fast as a shorebird?	☐	☐
Will we be invited to a birthday party for a turtle?	☐	☐
Can hornets sting and hurt if you are teasing them?	☐	☐
Can a stork discover a turtle in the bathtub?	☐	☐
Would you furnish a tiny shack with thirty pink carpets?	☐	☐
Can you see the stars glitter and sparkle when it gets dark?	☐	☐

the word that matches the picture.

nasty nutshell nurse	normal northern nonsense
handle hammer hammock	startle turtle turkey
third Thursday thorny	morbid mermaid nevermore
thirteen shirtsleeve thirty	backward blackbird blanket
sorry serpent surprise	thermal thirsty thrifty

Pick the best word to finish each sentence.

purse	shorter	barber
first	thirsty	birthday
ferns	butter	carport

He may visit a _____ if he needs his curls cut shorter.

When you feel _____ , it is a treat to drink water.

A _____ can hold cash and cards.

The fastest horse will win _____ prize.

A turtle has a much _____ tail than a tiger.

At a _____ party the presents are a surprise.

The forest has many leafy, green _____ growing in it.

X it.

Lord Peter likes to perch in the birdbath.	☐	
Lord Peter gave the purse to the birds.	☐	
The mermaid has curly hair and a skirt.	☐	
The mermaid has dirty yarn on her shirt.	☐	
The turtle has a surprise gift on its shell.	☐	
The turtle overturns the shelf in the hall.	☐	
We must hurry to class before the bell rings.	☐	
Harry and Weng perform for the class.	☐	
Gordon gets a surprise from the quick serpent.	☐	
Gordon gets a surprise from the squirting hose.	☐	
The blackbirds are perching on top of the barn.	☐	
The blackbirds are pecking at the birdbath.	☐	
The nursery has a furry carpet by the crib.	☐	
The nurse will serve a big cake for her birthday.	☐	

Write it, using a word with *er*, *ir*, or *ur*.

	_____
	_____
	_____
	_____
	_____
	_____
	_____

24

Lesson 4

wor says /wer/ as in <u>wor</u>k.

Read, write, and ◯ it.

word			
_____			
worm			
_____			
world			
_____			

war says /wor/ as in <u>war</u>m.

Read, write, and ◯ it.

warn			
_____			
wart			
_____			
warm			
_____			

wor says /wer/ as in <u>wor</u>k.

◯ the word that matches the picture.

worth   or   porch?

snored   or   world?

worry   or   stormy?

word   or   work?

war says /wor/ as in <u>war</u>m.

◯ the word that matches the picture.

swarm   or   smart?

warm   or   mark?

award   or   awake?

harm   or   warn?

Spell.   Write.

	w	n	ar	or	t	k	_____
	w	n	or	ee	d	b	_____
	u	w	or	ar	n	m	_____
	m	w	oa	or	lt	ld	_____
	w	m	or	ar	n	mt	_____
	sw	w	ar	ir	m	n	_____
	m	w	ea	ar	d	t	_____

Yes or no?

	Yes	No
Can a happy worm sing and warble a song?	☐	☐
If you work hard and train to run quickly, could you win the award?	☐	☐
Will a person do homework in the middle of a swarm of bees?	☐	☐
Is it worthwhile to have a warning of a storm before it strikes?	☐	☐
Are you likely to see a hammer and nails on a workbench?	☐	☐
Does a snowman have a warm nose and five fingers?	☐	☐
Can the world travel backward if you ask it to?	☐	☐

homeward workhorse homework	warfare warmer warrant
lifting thorny wordy	worthwhile worker worldwide
worker workbench workday	marble worldly wormy
deckhand backward backboard	firewood forward fireworks
wardrobe warship warning	swirl swarming warmer

Pick the best word to finish each sentence.

worry	swarming	warning
workhorse	worthwhile	workbench
warm	homework	award

A _____ pulls the hay wagon for the farmer at harvest time.

It is _____ to water your plants weekly.

It is _____ in the summer when the sun shines a long time.

Winning an _____ shows you did the best work on a project.

When I am sailing, I _____ about storm warnings.

The honeybees were _____ as they left the hive.

We study carefully in order to do our _____ well.

X it.

Chuck spells the list of words and gets the award.	☐	
Chuck can smell the worms in the warm garden.	☐	
Margo warns us to watch for a swarm of bees.	☐	
Margo warns us to wait for a warm day to swim.	☐	
The worst king became a toad with warts.	☐	
The worst king and the dragon are at war.	☐	
The password gets Shirley inside the workshop.	☐	
The patchwork quilt helps Shirley win the award.	☐	
The blackbird can warble from the treetop.	☐	
The blackboard has a warning about tardiness.	☐	
That workhorse is the shortest in the world.	☐	
That workbench has a worm inside it.	☐	
Carl got no reward for the worst sports car.	☐	
Carl worked to make a grand shortcake.	☐	

Write it, using a word with *wor* or *war*.

	_____
	_____
	_____
	_____
	_____
	_____
	_____

Read, write, and ⬭ it.

acorn			
_____			
barking			
_____			
corner			
_____			
warning			
_____			
birchbark			
_____			
serpent			
_____			
burst			
_____			

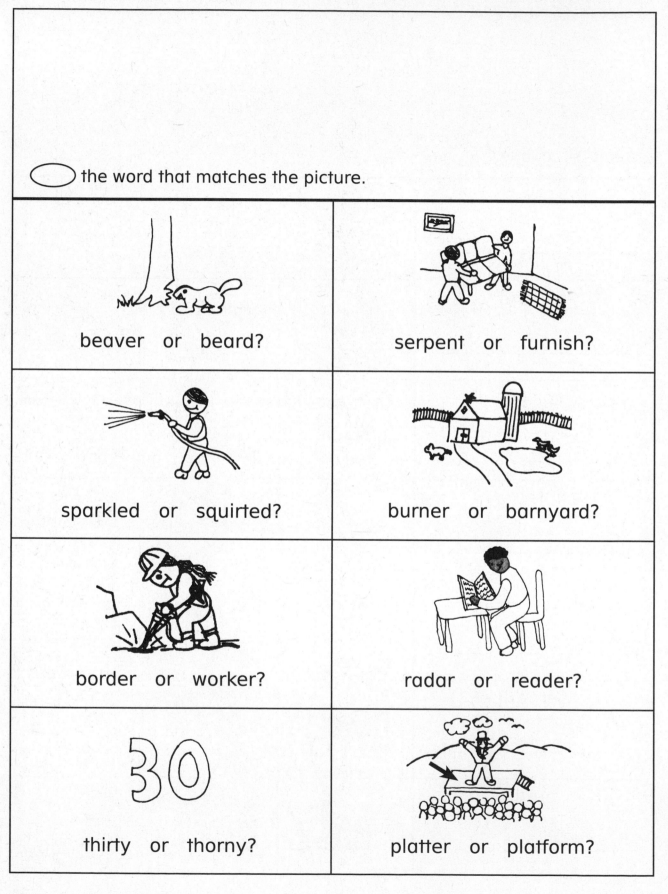

◯ the word that matches the picture.

beaver   or   beard?

serpent   or   furnish?

sparkled   or   squirted?

burner   or   barnyard?

border   or   worker?

radar   or   reader?

30

thirty   or   thorny?

platter   or   platform?

34

	Spell.		Write.
	car	cor	pet	port	_____
	bird	dirt	bash	bath	_____
	fan	lan	tern	torn	_____
	stor	slar	vy	y	_____
	mom	mon	stare	ster	_____
	fun	sun	burn	barn	_____
	cor	car	ner	mar	_____

35

Yes or no?

	Yes	No
Will a beaver furnish its home with a lantern?	☐	☐
Can you read a story that tells of a mean monster and a brave hero?	☐	☐
Does a serpent travel with a scarf and turtleneck shirt?	☐	☐
Will robins be chirping and splashing in the birdbath in March?	☐	☐
Do the actors in a play stand and speak from a platform?	☐	☐
Can a paper clip get a sunburn on a sandy beach?	☐	☐
Is it fun to see a porcupine and a panther play with marbles?	☐	☐

○ the word that matches the picture.

brushes bursting burden	dirt direct distant
charming snorkel charcoal	fort forbid forecast
quicksand whirlwind worthwhile	morsel snoring nurse
alarm armor aloft	wormhole worldwide workweek
pattern panther partner	turtle turnip fortune

Pick the best word to finish each sentence.

porcupine	swarming	paper clip
fingernails	fortune	birchbark
remark	actor	turtleneck

The _____ puts on a costume for the play.

On your hands you have ten _____ , which can get dirty.

The teacher uses a _____ to keep homework papers together.

A _____ has sharp quills, which can hurt your skin.

The bees are _____ around the new hive as we approach.

A shirt may have a _____ to help keep your neck snug and warm.

A birch tree is covered with _____ , which protects it as it grows.

X it.

The mummy needs to cut his long fingernails.	☐	
The mummy puts his thirteen fingers on the trombone.	☐	
King Arthur is surprised by the fortune in the trunk.	☐	
King Arthur is surprised by the truck in the fortress.	☐	
A serpent has a picnic by the birdbath.	☐	
The birds like to picnic in the bathtub.	☐	
The actor in the play is barking like a dog.	☐	
The actor in the play is working in darkness.	☐	
There is an acorn inside the lantern in the park.	☐	
The actor is swinging on the lantern in the park.	☐	
At home the girls are reading a story on the carpet.	☐	
The girls squirted the garden with the long hose.	☐	
The porcupine gets the award at the party.	☐	
The beaver sets the alarm in the corner.	☐	

Write it.

	_____
	_____
	_____
	_____
	_____
	_____
	_____

40

Lesson 6

igh says /ī/ as in *light*.
The *gh* is silent.

Read, write, and ⬭ it.

right			
_____			
night			
_____			
high			
_____			
sight			
_____			
bright			
_____			
fright			
_____			
tight			
_____			

igh says /ī/ as in *light*.

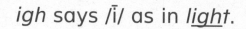 the word that matches the picture.

flight   or   fit?

high   or   highness?

sigh   or   sight?

tight   or   tiger?

right   or   rush?

midnight   or   midway?

frighten   or   fighter?

tighten   or   twilight?

left right	r	h	ee igh	t	d	_____
	k	l	igh ai	m	t	_____
	m	n	oa igh	b	t	_____
	sh	t	ir igh	t	r	_____
	br	b	igh ea	t	f	_____
	fr	tr	igh i	k	t	_____
	sw	s	ai igh	t	n	_____

Yes or no?

	Yes	No
Can you drive a sports car on a highway at twilight?	☐	☐
Can you sleep overnight on a bunk bed?	☐	☐
Is a flashlight brighter than a candle?	☐	☐
Does lightning in a storm frighten you a lot?	☐	☐
Will sunlight shine warmly at midnight?	☐	☐
Are you right to say ten plus ten is sixteen?	☐	☐
Is a windmill on a farm higher than an anthill?	☐	☐

the word that matches the picture.

midship	tighten
midyear	tigress
midnight	Titanic
fighting	flight deck
fainting	flashlight
frighten	flashback
sunlight	spotless
delight	spotlight
sublime	sportscast
timber	brightness
lightbulb	bring
tightrope	bridesmaid
lightest	deliver
lightning	delight
lively	defrost

45

Pick the best word to finish each sentence.

lightning	tightrope	brightest
flight	right	flashlight
night	highness	sigh

The acrobat rides a bike on a high _____ .

During a storm there is sometimes thunder and
_____ with rain.

We get up in the morning and go to bed at _____ .

Do you make a wish when you are the first to see the
_____ star of the night?

If it is dark at midnight, you may need a _____ .

Do not turn left, turn _____ .

After a long _____ , the airplane landed
in Nome, Alaska.

X it.

| The sports car is going north on the highway. ☐ | |
| The short cat is sneaking to a higher branch. ☐ | |

| Her highness will light the lantern. ☐ | |
| The selfish little girl has a light bundle. ☐ | |

| The sky is bright with sunlight. ☐ | |
| The lightning brightens the sky. ☐ | |

| Mark tightens the ropes on the sailboat. ☐ | |
| Mark holds the dog as he slides on the tightrope. ☐ | |

| The tiger and the smart girl dine by candlelight. ☐ | |
| The smart girl lights a candle on the birthday cake. ☐ | |

| The fighter is wishing that he will be a winner. ☐ | |
| The tiger with whiskers will frighten the children. ☐ | |

| The brightest student in the class wins the award. ☐ | |
| That student has the brightest wardrobe. ☐ | |

Write it, using a word with *igh*.

left right	
	_____
	_____
	_____
	_____
	_____
	_____
	_____

Lesson 7

oo says two things:
Sometimes oo says /$\overline{oo}$/ as in _boot_.
Sometimes oo says /$\breve{oo}$/ as in _book_.

Read, write, and ⬭ it.

foot			
_____			
cook			
_____			
broom			
_____			
moon			
_____			
spoon			
_____			
roof			
_____			
goose			
_____			

oo says /o͞o/ as in *bo͞ot*.
oo says /o͝o/ as in *bo͝ok*.

the word that matches the picture.

good or goose?

hook or shook?

food or foot?

stool or stoop?

tooth or troop?

mood or moose?

booth or boot?

soot or shoot?

	b d	oo oa	g k	_____
	n m	oo oi	n m	_____
	st sp	ea oo	k n	_____
	br dr	oo oe	k m	_____
	g f	o oo	t d	_____
	r gr	u oo	t f	_____
	g j	or oo	t se	_____

Yes or no?

	Yes	No
Does sandpaper feel smooth in the morning?	☐	☐
Can a poodle catch a football in the dark?	☐	☐
Will a woolly hood keep you warm in winter?	☐	☐
Is it spooky in a dark, wooded forest?	☐	☐
Are you foolish to ride home on a broomstick?	☐	☐
Is a spoonful of root beer a good cure for a sick hamster?	☐	☐
Have you understood this lesson so far?	☐	☐

the word that matches the picture.

moon	rooky
meet	rootless
moose	rooftop
teaspoon	toolbox
teasing	toothbrush
harpoon	tooting
football	poodle
foolish	puddle
footprints	poolside
woolly	cooling
woodpile	crooked
wedding	cookbook
booklet	footloose
bookshelf	football
brooding	foothill

Pick the best word to finish each sentence.

moose	playroom	toolbox
rooftop	cookbook	understood
toothbrush	goodness	pool

When you are fixing supper, you may need to use a
_____ .

The foolish _____ is eating grass behind
the woodpile.

On a hot summer day, swimming in a _____
cools me off.

The repair person came with a _____ to
fix the TV.

To keep your teeth clean you must use your _____
after every meal.

The snow on the _____ shines in the bright
moonlight.

Put the toys in the _____ .

X it.

The hungry football player is looking for some French food.	☐	
The French cook is reading the cookbook.	☐	
The football fell on the crooked rooftop.	☐	
The goose stood on the crooked bookshelf.	☐	
Mike is snooping into the chicken coop.	☐	
Mike is stooping to look at the footprints.	☐	
The woolly poodle has a boot on its right foot.	☐	
The frightened poodle stood and shook as I read the book.	☐	
Betsy understood the textbook.	☐	
Betsy inspects the spooky room.	☐	
The foolish groom has a loose tooth.	☐	
The food falls in the pool.	☐	
The moose is tooting its horn in the moonlight.	☐	
The raccoon is barking at the moose.	☐	

Write it, using a word with *oo*.

spoon	_____
broom	_____
MOTHER GOOSE	_____
foot	_____
moon	_____
boot	_____
roof	_____

Lesson 8

ea says two things:
Sometimes ea says /ē/ as in eat.
Sometimes ea says /ĕ/ as in head.

Read, write, and ◯ it.

feast			
_____			
thread			
_____			
sweat			
_____			
beard			
_____			
dead			
_____			
ear			
_____			
breath			
_____			

ea says /ē/ as in *eat*.
ea says /ĕ/ as in *head*.

 the word that matches the picture.

read or ride?

dead or deep?

beads or beard?

steak or sneak?

wheat or wealth?

peach or porch?

beast or best?

bread or beard?

	Spell.			Write.
	b　　d	ea　　oo	st　　ts	_____
	h　　n	ee　　ea	p　　d	_____
	br　　dr	ai　　ea	m　　n	_____
	dr　　d	ea　　i	b　　d	_____
	b　　p	ar　　ea	d　　rd	_____
	d　　b	ea　　ir	t　　d	_____
	thr　　th	ir　　ea	d　　p	_____

Yes or no?

	Yes	No
Can a dead beast squeal at a purple turtle?	☐	☐
Do you spread cream on your bread for breakfast?	☐	☐
Can you hear me speaking if you are deaf?	☐	☐
Will a dragon shave its beard with a spear?	☐	☐
Will you go sailing beyond the harbor in bad weather?	☐	☐
When it is very warm and the sun is high, will you sweat?	☐	☐
Does a goose in a meadow have lots of feathers?	☐	☐

 the word that matches the picture.

dreaming
defeat
dreadful

wealthy
weakness
weather

peanut
peacock
precook

heaven
heavy
healer

feather
farther
father

sweeter
swelter
sweater

squirting
squealing
squirrel

easel
meanwhile
measles

weeping
weasel
weapon

mellow
meadow
medal

Pick the best word to finish each sentence.

underneath	sweaty	deaf
meadow	healthy	bread
breath	ears	feathers

For a sandwich, she spread peanut butter and jelly on her

_____ .

When it is chilly and frosty, you can see the vapor of your

_____ .

The team was all hot and _____ after the
hard football game.

In wintertime, you put on a hat and scarf to keep your neck,
head, and _____ warm.

When you feel and look fine, the doctor says that you are

_____ .

The presents were stacked up _____ the
blanket to hide them.

Birds have plenty of _____ to help keep
them warm.

X it.

Tex is reading at the wedding.	☐	
Tex is reaching for his leather wallet.	☐	
The cat is romping in the pleasant meadow.	☐	
The shorebird is flying in the pleasant meadow.	☐	
The peacock has a flea on its feathered head.	☐	
The peacock spreads its tail feathers.	☐	
Mark wished his beard was as handsome as his pet's.	☐	
Mark wished for bread with cheddar cheese.	☐	
The moose eats a healthy snack.	☐	
The moose is dreaming of a cool, shady tree.	☐	
It is easy to hear that screaming.	☐	
The eagle likes to splash in the stream.	☐	
David sneaks up behind the beast.	☐	
The beast is stealing David's bread.	☐	

Write it, using a word with *ea*.

	_____
	_____
	_____
	_____
	_____
	_____
	_____

ie says two things:
Sometimes ie says /ī/ as in p**ie**.
Sometimes ie says /ē/ as in police ch**ie**f.

Read, write, and ◯ it.

tie			
_____			
pie			
_____			
lie			
_____			
field			
_____			
grief			
_____			
shield			
_____			
chief			
_____			

ie says /ī/ as in p*ie*.
ie says /ē/ as in police ch*ie*f.

 the word that matches the picture.

sheep   or   shield?

yell   or   yield?

die   or   day?

lie   or   load?

brief   or   breath?

windshield   or   wind?

green   or   grief?

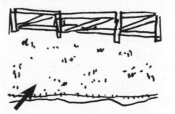

field   or   feel?

66

	gr	ch	ei	ie	f	p	_____
	p	b	ie	ea			_____
	h	f	ea	ie	p	d	_____
	d	t	ie	ee			_____
	h	f	ie	a	ld	it	_____
	ch	f	oo	ie	th	f	_____
	ch	sh	ie	igh	lp	ld	_____

Yes or no?

	Yes	No
Can the chief pull a thread from his sweater?	☐	☐
Can the shortstop eat apple pie in right field?	☐	☐
Can a rainstorm with thunder and lightning be brief?	☐	☐
Does a farmer work in the field with a briefcase?	☐	☐
Can a poodle tie its leash to a woodpile?	☐	☐
Will you serve pie or birthday cake on a silver shield?	☐	☐
Will a fire chief wear leather boots?	☐	☐

the word that matches the picture.

	until untie untidy		thief think thread
	pie crust poolside pineapple		bookcase briefcase breakfast
	mischief handkerchief handlebar		father feather fielder
	canary campfire camera		nickel tieback necktie
	sweeter sweater swelter		windmill watershed windshield

69

Pick the best word to finish each sentence.

windshield	airfield	pie
chiefly	believe	necktie
tied	brief	handkerchief

If you eat apple _____ outside, watch out for the flies.

When it starts to rain, we turn on the car's _____ wipers.

Can you tie your own _____ under a shirt collar?

I don't _____ your canary can talk.

The plane landed safely with the help of spotlights on the _____ .

When you have a runny nose, you need a _____ .

The captain lowered the sails and then _____ the sailboat to the dock.

X it.

The chief is baking bread with yeast.	☐	
The chief is heaping up the meatballs.	☐	
The eagle swoops at the windshield.	☐	
The windshield is covered with soot.	☐	
David ran thirty yards on the football field.	☐	
The healthy baby kicks the ball in the backyard.	☐	
Ricardo tied his necktie to the flagpole.	☐	
Ricardo tried to make mudpies in the sandbox.	☐	
The sneaky thief is reaching into the briefcase.	☐	
The thief is hoping to sneak away with the baked goods.	☐	
Sally waves her handkerchief at the beast.	☐	
Sally drops her handkerchief on the beach.	☐	
In this weather, the highway looks like a mudpie.	☐	
Walter makes mudpies at the baseball field.	☐	

Write it, using a word with *ie*.

	_____
	_____
	_____
	_____
	_____
	_____
	_____

Lesson 10 • Review Lesson

Read, write, and ⬭ it.

stool _____			
zoo _____			
leash _____			
hood _____			
stream _____			
high _____			
sweater _____			

the word that matches the picture.

shook or sock?	Pookie or spooky?
sneak or snack?	boost or boots?
stool or tools?	peas or pies?
sigh or sight?	peach or patch?

	neck reck	toe tie	_____
	fight foot	print paint	_____
	farth feath	est er	_____
	tooth tight	brush bush	_____
	sweat sweet	ly er	_____
	sleep stoop	ing ling	_____
	Spain spoon	ful fy	_____

Yes or no?

	Yes	No
Does a baby goose believe in mermaids?	☐	☐
Will a book enjoy sightseeing at the zoo?	☐	☐
Do cooks sometimes use leather to make pumpkin pie?	☐	☐
Does Pookie travel on a broomstick to visit his pals?	☐	☐
Could you order a cone with three scoops?	☐	☐
Does fresh peach pie taste good at the end of a feast?	☐	☐
Will the repair person use tools and a flashlight to fix the leaking pipes?	☐	☐

the word that matches the picture.

footnote foolproof footprints	dashboard flashlight flat-footed
father farther feather	stooping stopping standing
daylight limelight moonlight	highness highchair tightness
sponsor spoonful spotlight	sightless sightseeing slightly
breadstick bedspread bandstand	beardless breathless breadboard

77

Pick the best word to finish each sentence.

bedspread	mudpies	sightseeing
weather	hood	stooping
moonlight	breathless	sweater

I smoothed the blankets on my bed and then put on the
_____ .

We have not yet seen the sights of Atlanta, so we are going
_____.

The athlete is _____ after running six miles.

Jeanie is _____ down to pick up the paper
she dropped.

The TV forecasts said the _____ today would
be cool and rainy.

When the weather is chilly, I pull up the _____
of my jacket.

My little sister likes to use a shovel in the sandbox and make
_____ .

X it.

Rachel took a breathful of air and threw herself into the pool.	☐	
The hound is breathless from swimming around the pond.	☐	
The cook sneaks into the moonlit room.	☐	
The cook speaks to the roomful of nurses.	☐	
The breathless fighter slumps in his corner.	☐	
The frightened sailor stoops to pick up the beads.	☐	
Rozell is delighted when she wins tickets to a football game.	☐	
Russell squealed with delight when we tickled his foot.	☐	
The windmill is higher than the trees.	☐	
Her highness stood on top of the broomstick.	☐	
The crook scooped the tools into a loose bag.	☐	
The cook stacks her pies on the crooked stool.	☐	
In the middle of the woods stood a porcupine.	☐	
The tin woodman picked a peach and started eating it.	☐	

Write it.

	_____
	_____
	_____
	_____
	_____
	_____
	_____

Lesson 11

Read, write, and ⬭ it.

Roy			
_____			
joint			
_____			
join			
_____			
joy			
_____			
point			
_____			
noisy			
_____			
annoy			
_____			

oi and *oy* say /oy/ as in b<u>oi</u>l and b<u>oy</u>.

○ the word that matches the picture.

coy   or   coin?

bay   or   boy?

tie   or   toil?

took   or   toy?

broom   or   broil?

destroy   or   royal?

soil   or   shoot?

coil   or   coal?

82

		Spell.		Write.
	f t	oi oy		_____
5¢	c p	oi oy	m n	_____
	d b	oi oo	k l	_____
	f j	oi oy		_____
	g j	oi oy	lt nt	_____
MOTHER GOOSE	d b	oy oo	ch k	_____
	p j	oy oi	m n	_____

Yes or no?

	Yes	No
Will the baby be spoiled if he gets lots of toys?	☐	☐
Do you enjoy reading in a room that is messy and noisy?	☐	☐
Can foil be used to keep food fresh and moist?	☐	☐
Is a coin so heavy that a child will drop it?	☐	☐
Will a joyful poodle broil meat on a grill?	☐	☐
Should Roy use a bandage and ointment on a cut?	☐	☐
Would you plant poison ivy in your garden?	☐	☐

◯ the word that matches the picture.

injure	oyster
enjoy	overturn
jointly	oilskin

painted	toot
jointed	togs
pointed	toys

boyish	spoil
brooding	spoon
broiling	spool

coin	pantry
color	destroy
cage	royal

boiling	oilcan
briefcase	organize
breadboard	ointment

Pick the best word to finish each sentence.

joint	enjoy	royal
annoy	oily	boyish
foil	broiling	destroy

Roy is 30, but he is very _____ looking.

We use _____ to cover leftovers and keep them moist.

You burn charcoal in a grill when _____ hamburgers.

An athlete will _____ playing a soccer game with the winning team.

Noisy workers in the library will _____ the readers.

The bones of the arm form a _____ at the elbow.

If you push a heavy snowman over, you _____ it.

X it.

Tom pointed at the bright coins by the bread.	☐	
At night Tom points at a bright star that he can see from his bed.	☐	
The owl is boiling the oil over the campfire.	☐	
The owl joins a noisy gang on a summer night.	☐	
The boy is spoiling his pet pooch with treats.	☐	
The boy's tantrum has spoiled the party.	☐	
Your knee is the joint between your upper and lower leg.	☐	
I do not enjoy banging my elbow.	☐	
The baby has a raccoon that annoys Scott.	☐	
The girl is annoyed by the noisy boy on the train.	☐	
Jeff enjoys broiling hot dogs for his classmates.	☐	
Jeff joins his dog in the house with the pointed roof.	☐	
The coins make a fine noise as they hit the pavement.	☐	
The boys pay for the treat with thirteen silver coins.	☐	

87

Write it, using a word with *oi* or *oy*.

	_____
	_____
	_____
	_____
	_____
	_____
5¢	_____

Lesson 12

ou and sometimes *ow* say /ou/ as in m<u>ou</u>th and c<u>ow</u>.

Read, write, and ◯ it.

south _____			
mouse _____			
cow _____			
growl _____			
outside _____			
nightgown _____			
lighthouse _____			

89

ou and sometimes *ow* say /ou/ as in <u>mou</u>th and <u>cow</u>.

 the word that matches the picture.

round   or   road?

book   or   bow?

stool   or   stout?

coach   or   couch?

tower   or   towel?

brown   or   broom?

loud   or   lord?

looping   or   plowing?

90

	Spell.			Write.
	sl cl	ou oo	b d	_____
	ow oi	t l		_____
	m n	or ou	te th	_____
	b d	ow ar	k n	_____
	cr ch	oo ow	n u	_____
	sh s	oa ou	d th	_____
	gl cl	ow oo	m n	_____

Yes or no?

	Yes	No
Will a cow get a crown for eating the freshest flowers?	☐	☐
Does a clown act like a fool and jump up and down in the spotlight?	☐	☐
Is a brown mouse as big and heavy as the couch in the living room?	☐	☐
Does the little toy mouse clean your messy house with a broom and towel?	☐	☐
Can you see down to the ground from a lighthouse by the seashore?	☐	☐
Do owls make spooky noises outside at night?	☐	☐
Is it cloudy and damp in the garden during a rain shower?	☐	☐

the word that matches the picture.

topsoil tower towel	foolish founding flounder
cower couch county	crooked clouded crowded
noontime moody moonlight	grounded roomed rounded
shower shouted scouting	cloudy lower loudest
outstanding frowning crowing	foulest floater flower

93

Pick the best word to finish each sentence.

counted	growling	towel
allow	drowsy	mouthful
found	cloudy	thousand

If your cute pet is lost, you are glad when it is finally

_____ .

After a shower or swim in the pool, we use a _____
to get dry.

The clown felt very _____ when it was
past his bedtime.

If you have a _____ of food and try to talk,
you might choke.

On a _____ day you cannot see the
bright sunlight.

A _____ is a big number that has three
zeros at the end.

A dog that is _____ can frighten even
a brave person.

X it.

Joy looks outside the house at the pile of coins.	☐	
Joy looks in the round house for the pile of toys.	☐	
The clown has a squirting flower on her head.	☐	
The clown has a squeaking mouse on her head.	☐	
Roy shouts from the lighthouse when it gets cloudy.	☐	
Roy plays the trumpet louder than the rest of the crowd.	☐	
The poodle is growling at the brown trout.	☐	
The trout by the river frowns at the crowd.	☐	
The cow has a mouthful of ferns for supper.	☐	
The couch is covered with a shower of ferns.	☐	
The owl is throwing the crown at the king's throne.	☐	
The owl with the crown is perched on the throne.	☐	
The mouse enjoys the noise from the loud bulldozer.	☐	
The boy with the hammer is frowning at the loud bulldozer.	☐	

95

Write it, using a word with *ou* or *ow*.

	_____
	_____
	_____
	_____
	_____
	_____
	_____

Lesson 13

au and aw say /aw/ as in <u>hau</u>l and <u>saw</u>.

Read, write, and ◯ it.

paw			
lawn			
shawl			
jaw			
hawk			
yawn			
claw			

au and *aw* say /aw/ as in *h<u>au</u>l* and *s<u>aw</u>*.

 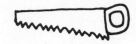

 the word that matches the picture.

claw   or   clay?

Paul   or   powder?

pow   or   paw?

found   or   fawn?

dawn   or   down?

boil   or   draw?

auto   or   howl?

August   or   awful?

98

	Spell.			Write.
	y h	aw ow	t k	_____
	br dr	oy aw		_____
	cr cl	aw ou	d l	_____
	w y	ai aw	m n	_____
	st sh	a aw	l mp	_____
	h n	au oi	l t	_____
	str shr	oy aw		_____

Yes or no?

	Yes	No
Can a hawk do its laundry in the birdbath?	☐	☐
Do you think Paul enjoys playing on a seesaw on the lawn?	☐	☐
Can an auto crawl faster than a grasshopper can hop?	☐	☐
Is it helpful to use a lawnmower to trim the grass?	☐	☐
Can you polevault with a drinking straw?	☐	☐
Is it your fault if you yawn each day in class?	☐	☐
Will you squawk if you get coleslaw for supper?	☐	☐

the word that matches the picture.

outfield

outlaw

outdoor

awning

lawful

awful

poolside

polevault

polecat

loudest

laundry

lawmaker

thawing

thinning

yawning

awkward

autumn

August

sprawling

scrawling

sawing

seashore

seedling

seesaw

lawyer

launching

lawnmower

author

aunt

Pick the best word to finish each sentence.

drawing	thawing	yawning
lawnmower	autumn	claws
outlaw	sawing	coleslaw

The season when the leaves fall from the trees is

_____ .

The lumberjack has cut some logs and is _____
them to make boards.

In summer we trim the grass around the house with a

_____.

When I am sleepy, you will see me _____.

In the spring when the snow is melting, we say it is

_____.

A person acting outside the law in the old West was called

an _____ .

When the eagle saw the food, it used its _____
to pick it up.

X it.

Paul made a drawing of an autumn leaf.	☐	
Paul's auto makes an awful noise on the highway.	☐	
The moose is sprawling on the lawn.	☐	
The moon is spraying moonbeams at dawn.	☐	
The hawk has its claws on the mouse.	☐	
The mouse is crawling up to the author's house.	☐	
Paula is sipping a milk shake with a straw.	☐	
The straw is slipping down from the hayloft.	☐	
The lawnmower got tangled with the laundry.	☐	
The laundry is flapping in the autumn wind.	☐	
The poodle sinks its jaws into the raw meat.	☐	
The snow is melting and thawing into puddles on the lawn.	☐	
The crow is yawning and squawking.	☐	
The cow is sprawled in a heap of straw.	☐	

Write it, using a word with *aw*.

	_____
	_____
	_____
	_____
	_____
	_____
	_____

Lesson 14

ew, ui, ue, and sometimes *ou* say /ōō/ as in s*ui*t.

Read, write, and ◯ it.

fruit			
_____			
group			
_____			
stew			
_____			
blew			
_____			
soup			
_____			
new			
_____			
flew			
_____			

ew, ui, ue, and sometimes *ou* say /o͞o/ as in *suit*.

 the word that matches the picture.

blue or boo?

news or noise?

yarn or youth?

crowd or cruise?

suit or soup?

screw or stew?

glue or grew?

true or threw?

Spell.   Write.

	z s	ou oi	t p	_____
	fr gr	au ui	d t	_____
	sh s	ow ui	t p	_____
	bl dl	aw ew		_____
	gr br	aw ou	q p	_____
	ch sh	ew oe		_____
	m n	ow ew		_____

Yes or no?

	Yes	No
Can you eat soup with a long screwdriver?	☐	☐
Will you put on a new suit before you button it?	☐	☐
Do you put glue on a broken toy to fix it?	☐	☐
Do you enjoy playing soccer with a group of boys and girls?	☐	☐
Will a leather suitcase be put in a sloppy stew?	☐	☐
Can a marble statue chew fruit?	☐	☐
If you bruise and scrape your arm, do you put ointment on it?	☐	☐

clawing choosing chewing	frustrate frowning fruitcake
silkworm screwdriver screamed	coiling soiled cruising
wanted wooded wounded	strewn seaweed stewed
brewing blue jay bluebell	sorrow suitcase suitable
newspaper newsboy newsstand	scribble scrapbook scarecrow

Pick the best word to finish each sentence.

overdue	statue	cruel
chewing	bluebird	withdrew
suitcase	screwdriver	newspaper

When you get ready to go on a trip, you pack your things in a
_____ .

If a screw is loose, you will need a _____
to fix it.

The stone figure in the park is called a _____ .

If you see something with lovely blue feathers flying in the sky,
it may be a _____ .

Do you have a _____ delivered to your
house every morning?

If you do not return your book to the library within three weeks,
it will be _____ .

The rabbit is _____ the raw carrot noisily.

X it.

The statue drew the drapes in the drawing room.	☐	
The statue has a bluebird on it.	☐	
The bluebird flew over the rainbow.	☐	
The rainbow grew fainter and fainter.	☐	
The group went on a cruise together.	☐	
The goose is cruising on a banana boat.	☐	
The youth threw the glue in the soup.	☐	
The soup grew too cool for Goldilocks.	☐	
Sue blew out the birthday candles.	☐	
Sue is holding the chewed fruit.	☐	
Uncle Lou stoops to pick up his new suit.	☐	
Lou spills soup on his uncle's new suit.	☐	
The fattest fruit grew on the peach tree.	☐	
A few trees were cut and used to construct a cabin.	☐	

Write it, using a word with *ew*, *ui*, or *ou*.

	_____ ew _____
	_____ ui _____
	_____ ui _____
	_____ ou _____
	_____ ou _____
	_____ ew _____
	_____ ew _____

Read, write, and ⬭ it.

trombone _____			
glue _____			
notebook _____			
baboon _____			
sawdust _____			
jewel _____			
flounder _____			

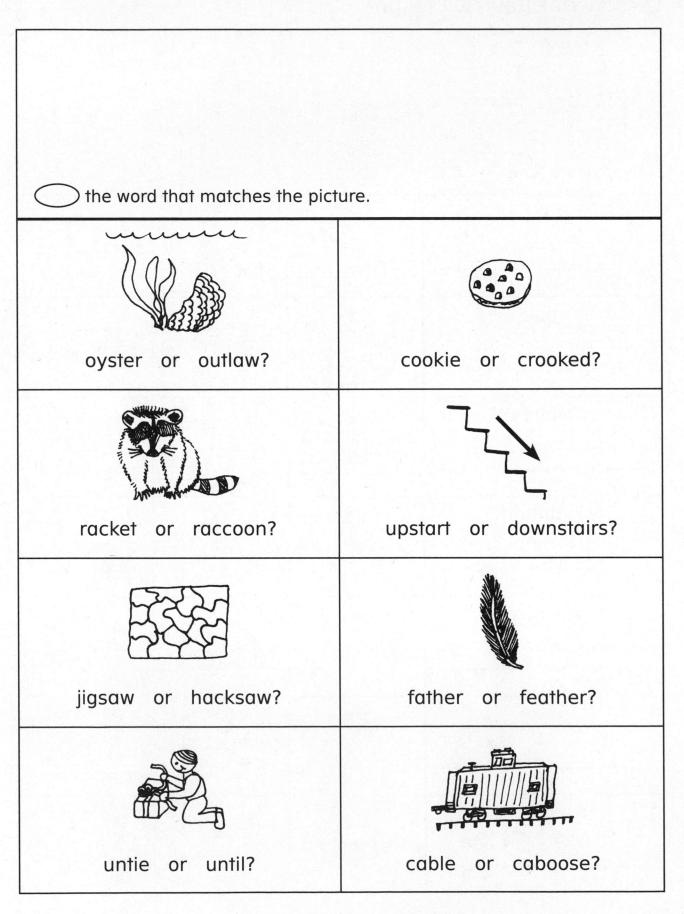

◯ the word that matches the picture.

oyster   or   outlaw?

cookie   or   crooked?

racket   or   raccoon?

upstart   or   downstairs?

jigsaw   or   hacksaw?

father   or   feather?

untie   or   until?

cable   or   caboose?

Spell. Write.

	saw sow	dust desk	_____
	nout note	bute book	_____
	rac raic	coon cone	_____
	ow oy	ster ters	_____
	coot cook	ie oy	_____
	pret prew	zel tel	_____
	snaw snow	flack flake	_____

Yes or no?

	Yes	No
Will a broken cookie crumble into bits?	☐	☐
Can a brass trombone be used to blow sweet music?	☐	☐
Can a raccoon finish a jigsaw puzzle?	☐	☐
Can you eat oyster stew with a teaspoon?	☐	☐
Are tasty pretzels made out of sawdust?	☐	☐
If you untie the ropes of a cruise ship, will it float away?	☐	☐
Can a baboon print its name on its homework and notebooks?	☐	☐

the word that matches the picture.

blue jay bluefish blueberry	lightheaded lightning lighthouse
barber barefoot barnstorm	boomerang bookcase bookmark
cracker crockery crocodile	forward firewood fireworks
clout county cloudy	moistened mouse hole mustard
igloo unglue goose	destiny destroy oyster

Pick the best word to finish each sentence.

countdown	sawdust	boyish
rooster	raccoon	igloo
barefoot	argue	shampoo

At dawn you can hear the _____ crowing.

When the lumberjack cuts wood with a chainsaw, the pile of _____ grows high.

Uncle Pete is a _____ man.

When your parents tell you to go to bed, you must not _____ with them.

Before the astronauts blast off, they will begin the _____ .

I like to walk _____ on the warm, sandy beach.

When I wash my hair, I use _____ that smells like flowers.

X it.

Jason is happy sauntering in the mud with his bare feet.	☐	
Staggering barefoot in the woods, Jason began to cry.	☐	
The silly raccoon is pretending to be a cowhand.	☐	
The rooster is trying to play with the raccoon's toys.	☐	
The raccoon will unhook the barnyard gate to free the roosters.	☐	
The president's navy blue necktie has a rooster on it.	☐	
Rosemary is grilling hamburgers on the barbecue.	☐	
Barbara is shaking hands with her new friend, Sir James Lion.	☐	
Homer is shampooing his black retriever.	☐	
Homer's retriever is taking a snooze on the couch.	☐	
Raymond is catching flounder in a frying pan.	☐	
Raymond is flying south with a flounder under his arm.	☐	
Andy is in the park ready to enjoy a pretzel from the pretzel wagon.	☐	
The baboon has hot pretzels and soup for lunch.	☐	

Write it.

	_____
	_____
	_____
	_____
	_____
	_____
	_____

Circle the 2 words in each box that have the same vowel sound.

1.	frown couch stoop	2.	field teach boast
3.	blessed green spread	4.	skirt glide slight
5.	moist oyster mouse	6.	shield churn third
7.	throat stoop flew	8.	shows groans blooms
9.	world snort churn	10.	thread chain paste
11.	fault train drawn	12.	fruit bloat gloom

◯ the word you hear.

1. squeaking swarming squirting scorching squirming	2. squawking sprawling sauntering sparkler spareribs
3. powerfully pound cake powdery powerless poverty	4. cheating chieftain chiefly cheapen cheesy
5. frightening freshest frightfulness friendless fretfulness	6. withstand withhold withers witness withdrew
7. northwest northwards northerly northeaster northlander	8. pheasant peasant pleasant plentiful planets
9. harpooned hairpinned happened harpsichord harmony	10. undertook undercooked understock understood understudy

1. _____

   _____

2. _____

   _____

3. _____

   _____

4. _____

   _____

5. _____

   _____

6. _____

   _____

Use the words to complete the sentences.

beach	foot	moonlit
shark	surf	sunburn
straw	necktie	proudly

1. On a _____ night Paul was swimming in the roaring _____. Suddenly he saw a monster fish gliding underneath his _____. It was a _____ with long, sharp teeth. The sight of that scary shark sent Paul quickly back to sit on the sandy _____.

burning	outdoors	lightning
warning	fireworks	tightrope
necktie	corner	handlebar

2. All of a sudden without any _____ there was a bang! Zap! Crackle! Bang! The loud noise shook the house. Howdy rushed _____ to see if _____ had struck the barn or if the house next door was _____. The night sky was bright with dazzling light and showers of sparks. Howdy was glad to see that it was just a _____ display.

trout	barefoot	sight
worms	threw	thread
sneakers	raccoon	broomstick

3. Rachel woke early in the morning, grabbed her sweater, and scampered into the field to dig up some _____. Next, she ran to the brook, took off her _____, and waded _____ into the water with her fishing rod and reel. Soon the skillful girl had a _____ on her line. She unhooked it and _____ it into a bucket. Then she returned to her fishing. At this point a hungry _____ appeared in the ferns near the bucket. Will this thief gobble down the fish before Rachel catches sight of him?